SAKURA

Three Koto Transcr~~iptions~~
for solo piano

Sakura Genso Kyoku by Chikushi Katsuko (1904-1984)
as performed by Keko Kanagawa
youtu.be/eZJ3TOKIy-Y

Sakura Henso Kyoku by Kimio Eto (1924-2012)
as performed by Shirley Kazuyo Muramoto
youtu.be/-wwV7QN186s

Sakura Sakura by Tadao Sawai (1937-1997)
as performed by Tadao Sawai
on the CD 箏 名曲選 ~ Koto Meikyoku Sen (The Best Selections of Koto Music)

Contents

Introduction

The Japanese *koto* (sometimes inexactly referred to as the Japanese harp) is a type of zither, a plucked string instrument where the strings stretch across the full length of a thin wooden body. It is descended from the Chinese *guzheng,* first imported into Japan in the 7th century. The most common type of modern *koto* is c.182cm long, has 13 silk strings of the same length and tension, with 13 moveable ivory bridges (one for each string) that allow for different tunings. The most common tunings are largely pentatonic in character and cover a range of 2 octaves and a fifth.

Koto transcriptions for piano

This collection of piano adaptations of three compositions for Japanese koto is intended to provide interested pianists (and other interested readers of western staff notation) a small insight into music for Japanese koto. The Japanese notated form of koto music is a tablature that includes string numbers (1-13) in Japanese and a form of rhythmic notation. However, there appears to be very little easily available koto music in western staff notation that captures more than simple versions of well-known melodies.

The purpose of this small book is to create a) a study tool to explore some of the different textures used by professional koto musicians, and b) performance sheet music for piano. It contains transcriptions of three beautiful performances of three distinct pieces composed by three influential 20th Century koto musicians—all based on the same well-known Japanese melody *Sakura* (Cherry Blossom). Each piece is for a 13-string *koto,* although each with a different tuning. A side by side comparison of these pieces serves to illustrate:

- some different textures characteristic of sophisticated koto music,
- a range of different methods of varying and decorating a pre-existing melody,
- different ways of structuring sets of variations, and
- some of the general aesthetics of traditional koto music in terms of its substantial use of flexible tempo (rubato), frequent textural changes, ornamentation, and dynamic contrasts.

Each performance has been carefully transcribed and then adapted to be performable on a piano. The change of medium results in a few necessary idiomatic adaptations for the piano; in particular, ornamentation such as mordents and grace notes is used where vibrato or portamento slides used on the koto cannot be directly replicated on the piano. I have however tried to keep these adaptations as close as possible to the recorded performances. This small project was undertaken largely for personal interest—in the spirit of exploring and gaining some appreciation of a distinctive and absolutely beautiful musical genre—and I hope it will be of interest to anyone similarly seeking a small insight into some wonderful koto music. I hope readers will agree that they make beautiful performance pieces on the piano.

How the koto is played

The koto lies horizontally on the floor, with the player sitting to one side at the end. Three plectrums *(tsume)* are worn on the thumb and first two fingers of the right hand. All fingers can be used to pluck the strings, with various techniques used to vary the timbre (eg: near plucking nearer or further away from the end of the string, and harmonics etc.). Importantly, vibrato and portamento-mordent ornamentation can be achieved by stretching or loosening the tension of the string using the left hand on the other side of the bridge—and this is an important characteristic of the overall sound of koto music. Additional pitches beyond the 13 can be achieved in this way, and sometimes compositions may also call for individual bridges to be moved mid-performance. Below is a list of some characteristic playing techniques:

- Tremolo—fast repetitions of a single pitch.
- *Yuri*—Vibrato—swinging the string on the other side of the bridge with the left hand.
- *Oshide*—Stretching a string (by pushing down on it with the left hand) and then plucking to create a single steady pitch a semitone or tone higher than the unstretched string would be.
- *Oshihibiki/Oshihanashi*—A portamento (slide) up/down effect, created by stretching/releasing the string with the left hand immediately after the string is plucked.
- *Tsukiiro*—A portamento upper mordent, achieved by stretching and immediately releasing the string after plucking it.

- *Hikiiro*—A similar, portamento lower mordent effect is achieved by reducing the tension of the plucked section of string by pulling the part of the string the other side of the bridge towards the bridge and then letting go.
- *Kakizume*—Plucking two neighbouring strings at once (sounding either pretty much simultaneous or one before the other) in a single stroke.
- *Oshiawase*—Plucking two neighbouring strings at once in a single stroke, but stretching the longer string (pushing down on it with the left hand) to match (more-or-less) the pitch of its neighbour.
- *Awasezume*—plucking chords (2 or 3 or more strings simultaneously, each with a different finger).
- *Chirashizume*—Scraping the string sideways (ending the movement by lifting the plectrum off the string) rather than plucking.
- *Keshizume*—Deadened, slightly buzzy note, plucked with the right hand but simultaneously muted with the finger-nail of the left hand.
- Staccato—plucked then vibrations immediately stopped with the left hand.
- Pizzicato—plucked directly with fingers (ie: not with plectrum)—this almost sounds like harmonics.
- Harmonics—plucked but with the left hand lightly touching the string at a precise point to produce a pitch an octave higher than the open string.
- *Sukuizume*—Plucking with the plectrum and immediately plucking back the other way with the other side of the plectrum (making a pair of short notes—both on the same string—the second tending to be quieter).

Sakura—Cherry Blossom

Sakura is an old folk-song of unknown origin about the blossom of the cherry tree. A version of its melody appeared—probably for the first time in western staff notation—in the Tokyo Academy of Music's 1888 publication *Collection of Japanese Koto Music,* edited by S. Isawa. This book is now in the public domain and its version of *Sakura* is included in full on the following page. The collection "consists of those pieces deemed suitable to serve as first steps to learning the Koto music", and this simple 14-bar melody is number 2 in the collection—ie: one of the simplest. It contains the sung melody with lyrics for verse 1, comprising seven 2-bar phrases (the first of which is one bar repeated), in the order ABCBCAD. The koto part is mostly the same except with three of the two-bar phrases up an octave, one extra note, finger numbers, and a 4-bar instrumental coda. *Hira-Joshi* is one of the common koto tunings, each string being numbered 1-13. The vocal melody is pentatonic, although the one extra note in the koto part is a sixth pitch. NB: The notation doesn't reflect idiomatic techniques such as vibrato or pitch bend (high C).

Shortly following the publication of that collection, various European composers began to use its melodies, often adding somewhat European harmonies. *Sakura* appears in André Messager's opera *Madame Chrysanthème* (1893), and was also one of numerous Japanese melodies in Giacomo Puccini's *Madame Butterfly* (1904). Francis Taylor Piggott provides a notated version of a similar popular piece *Saita-Sakurai* in his book *The Music and the Musical Instruments of Japan* (1893), along with his own added pianistic harmonies which he felt were implied by the tune. Rudolph Dittrich created a pianistic version of *Sakura* in *Nippon Gakufu, Six Japanese Popular Songs collected and arranged for the Pianoforte* (1894). A voice-plus-piano arrangement also appears in *One Hundred Folksongs of all Nations* (1911), edited by Granville Bantock. His accompanying notes state: "In Japan the season of the cherry-blossom is the occasion of a festival and holiday-making, and excursions take place to view the most favored localities throughout the country. There is much singing and rejoicing, the present song being a special favorite with the people, who are accustomed to sing it from childhood."

These publications are all now in the public domain (available from IMSLP and GoogleBooks), and I have included some images from relevant pages in the appendix (pages 31-34) to this book—useful as a study tool for comparing the pianistic textures added to a Japanese melody by European composers with actual koto textures composed by Japanese koto players.

How Sakura is used in the following three transcribed compositions

The following section outlines how the seven 2-bar phrases of the *Sakura* melody (ABCBCAD) are used in each of the pieces transcribed in this collection.

Sakura Genso Kyoku by Chikushi Katsuko, as performed by Keko Kanagawa

Bars

1-7	7 bar introduction—a decorative display of the range and tuning of the instrument.
8-21	Full 14-bar *Sakura* melody (ABCBCAD) with the final phrase slightly adapted. Often in octaves or simple harmony, plus one other accompanying layer.
22-29	Shortened 8-bar version (ABCA), with the melody frequently echoed at the octave in quavers.
30-41	Shortened 10-bar version (ABCAD), tremolo melody with repeated glissando accompaniment, ending with a decorative glissando into the tempo change.
42-57	New, double speed section reminiscent of the introduction.
58-73	Extended version of the full *Sakura* melody (ABCABCAD) at the same double speed, with busy semiquaver accompaniment.
74-77	Coda

Sakura Henso Kyoku by Kimio Eto, as performed by Shirley Kazuyo Muramoto

Bars

1-15   Full 14-bar *Sakura* melody (ABCBCAD), mostly with simple accompaniment, ending with tremolo and glissando.

16-31   Full 14-bar *Sakura* melody (ABCBCAD), with the melody decorated and often doubled, with more complex accompaniment. The final phrase is extended, again ending with tremolo and glissando.

32-46   Full 14-bar *Sakura* melody (ABCBCAD), with a string re-tuned to raise note 7 (in western terms) creating perfect cadences (V-I). The melody has simple decorations, with a single line accompaniment. Again the final phrase is extended, ending with a tremolo.

47-61   Full 14-bar *Sakura* melody (ABCBCAD), with busy decorations. Again the final phrase is extended.

61-69   Coda

Sakura Sakura (also known as *Two Variations*) composed and performed by Tadao Sawai

Bars

1-5   Introduction

6-20   Full 14-bar *Sakura* melody (ABCBCAD), with a variety of tremolo decorations and frequently changing accompaniment patterns (semiquavers/sextuplets/spread chords in the manner of slow harp glissandi), ending with additional bar.

21-35   Full 14-bar *Sakura* melody (ABCBCAD), with a faster accompaniment of a 3-semiquaver pattern of usually alternating adjacent strings, ending with an additional bar.

36-50   Full 14-bar *Sakura* melody (ABCBCAD) in a different key, slow, with sparse accompaniment, ending with an additional bar.

51-65   Full 14-bar *Sakura* melody (ABCBCAD), accompanied by fast 3-semiquaver runs, occasionally expanding to longer runs, ending with an additional bar.

66-89   ABCBCA, with very fast, almost double speed decoration in various octaves. For ease of reading, the melody note values are doubled—each 2-bar phrase now lasts 4 bars.

90-95   3 bars of dramatic glissandi, ending with the final very slow 2-bar phrase D.

If you have enjoyed exploring these pieces, you may also enjoy the following books by John Pitts:

Extreme Heterophony: a study in Javanese Gamelan for one or more pianists (2021), **How to Play Indian Sitar Rāgas on a Piano** (2020, 2nd edition), **Indian Rāgas for Piano made easy** (2020, 2nd edition), **Raga Jogiya Kalingra: Aroma of Saffron** (2020), **Pipa Dreams in Imperial Garden** (2018), **7 Piano Duets & Triets: inspired by music from around the world** (2016)

www.pianoraga.com

"Sakura Genso Kyoku"
by Chikushi Katsuko (1904-1984)

transcribed and adapted for piano by John Pitts from a performance by Keko Kanagawa

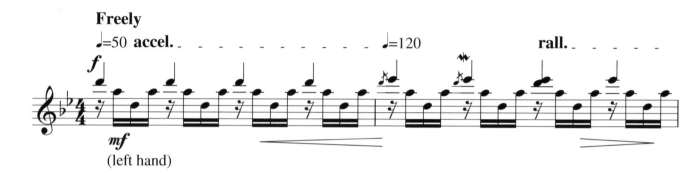

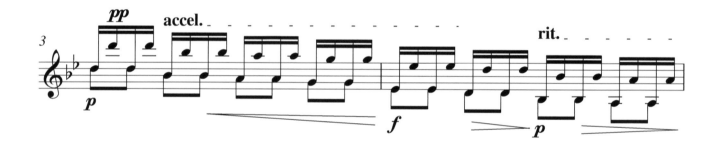

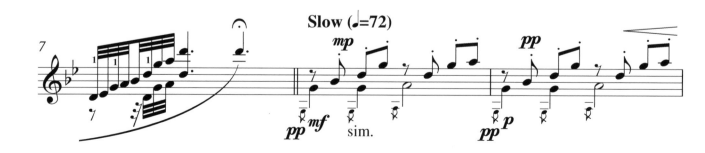

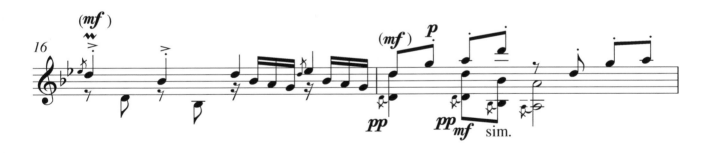

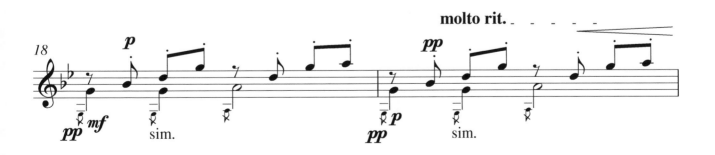

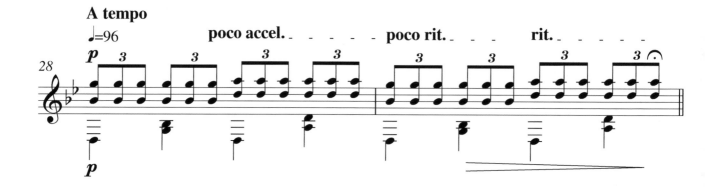

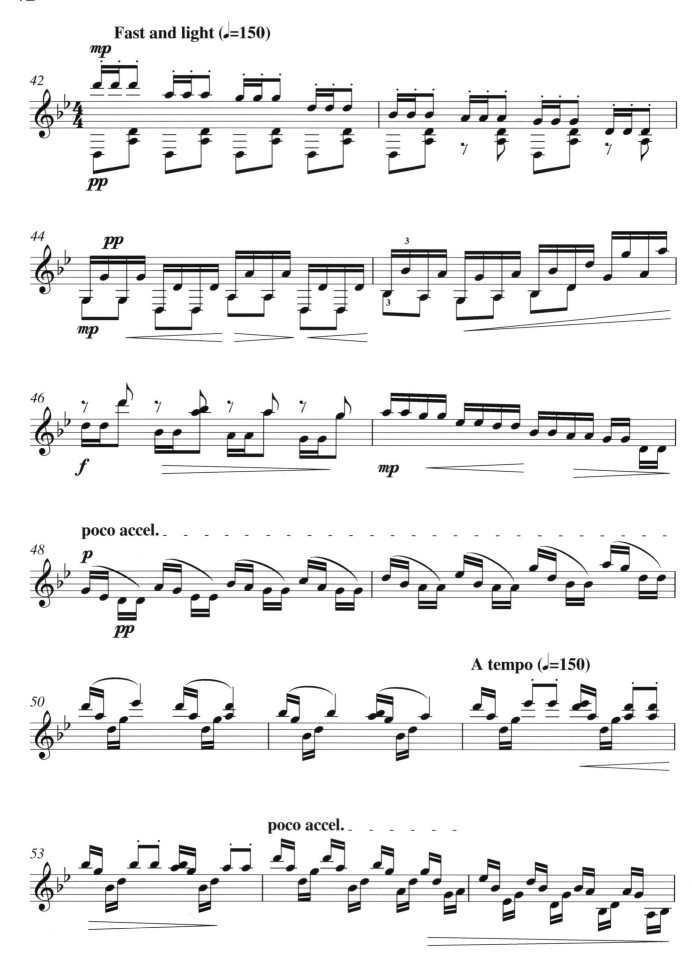

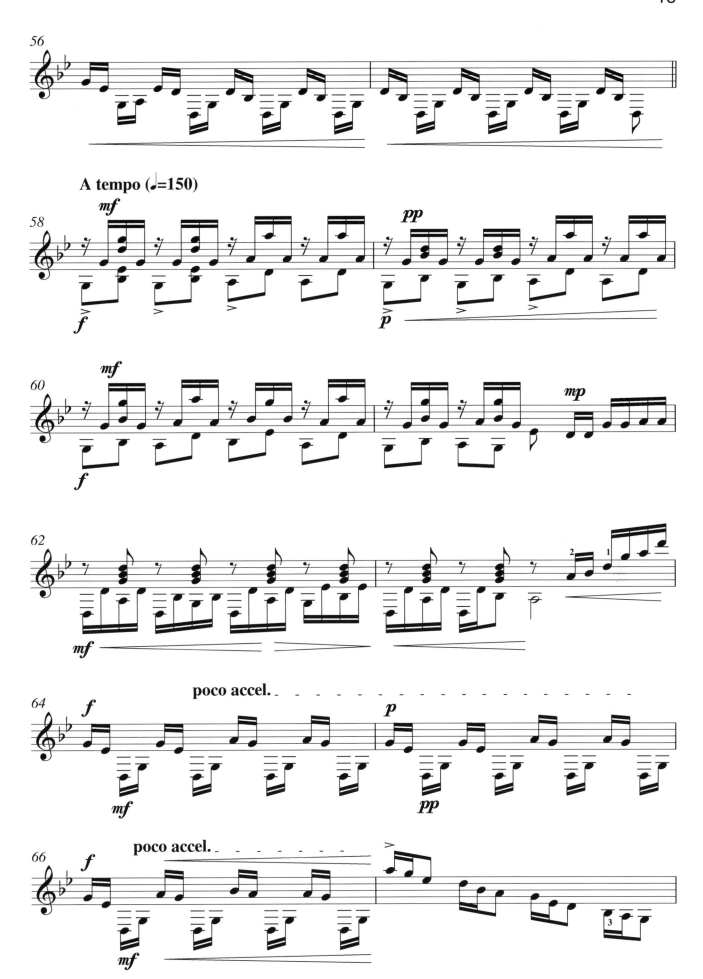

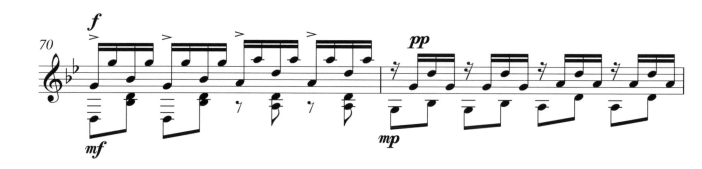

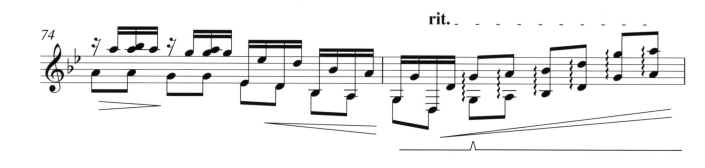

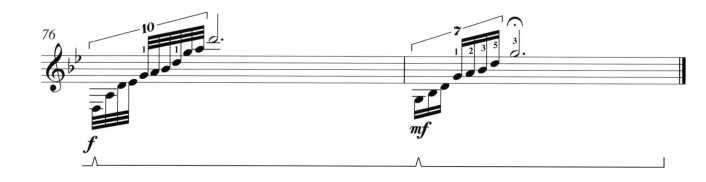

"Sakura Henso Kyoku"
by Kimio Eto (1924-2012)

transcribed and adapted for piano by John Pitts from a performance by Shirley Kazuyo Muramoto
(based on Ikuta Koto notated version and recording of Kimio Eto)

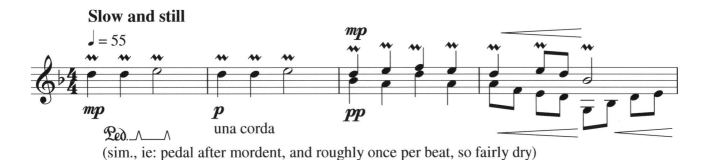

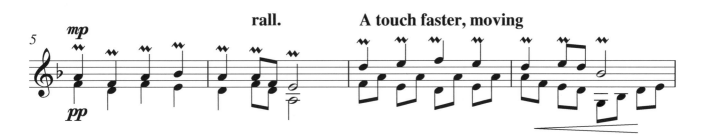

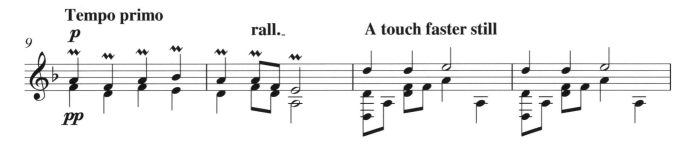

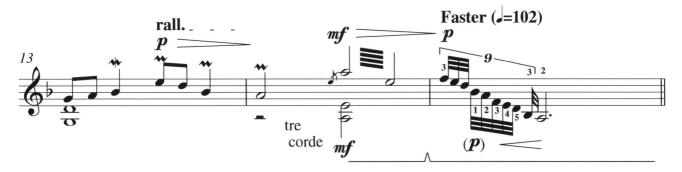

rall.

(retune 9B♭-C♯)

Slow, but a touch faster than tempo primo, moving

♩=60 *With purpose*

(some pedal, but fairly dry)

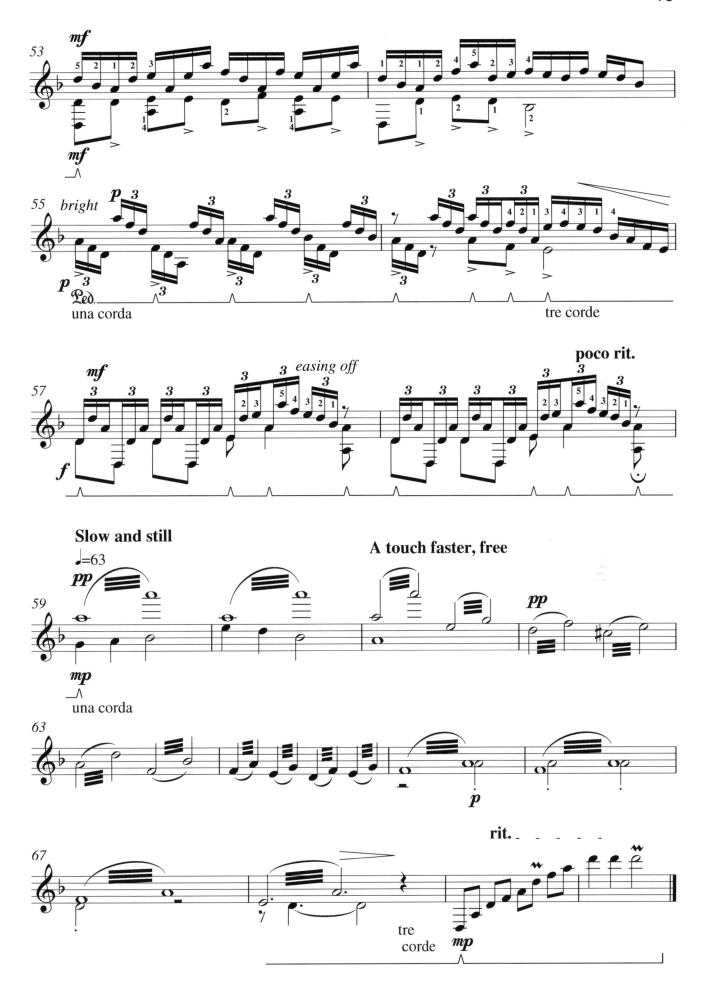

"Sakura Sakura"
by Tadao Sawai (1937-1997)

transcribed and adapted for piano by John Pitts from a performance by Tadao Sawai

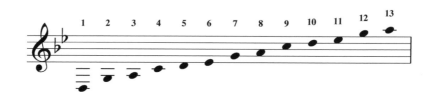

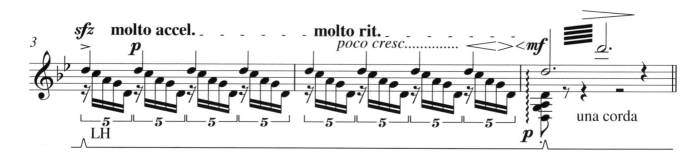

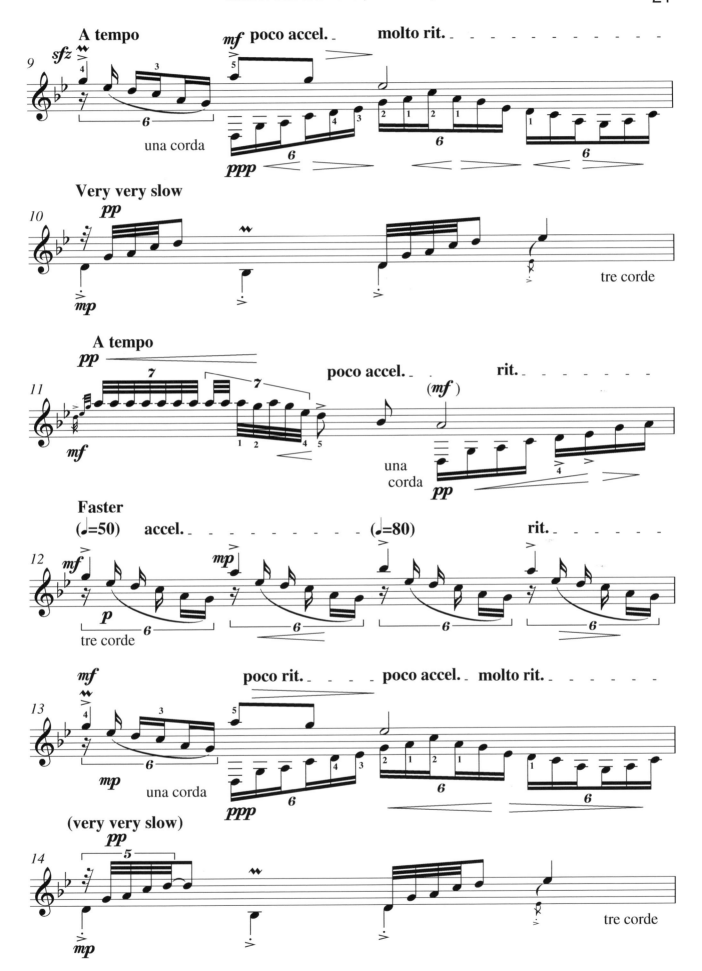

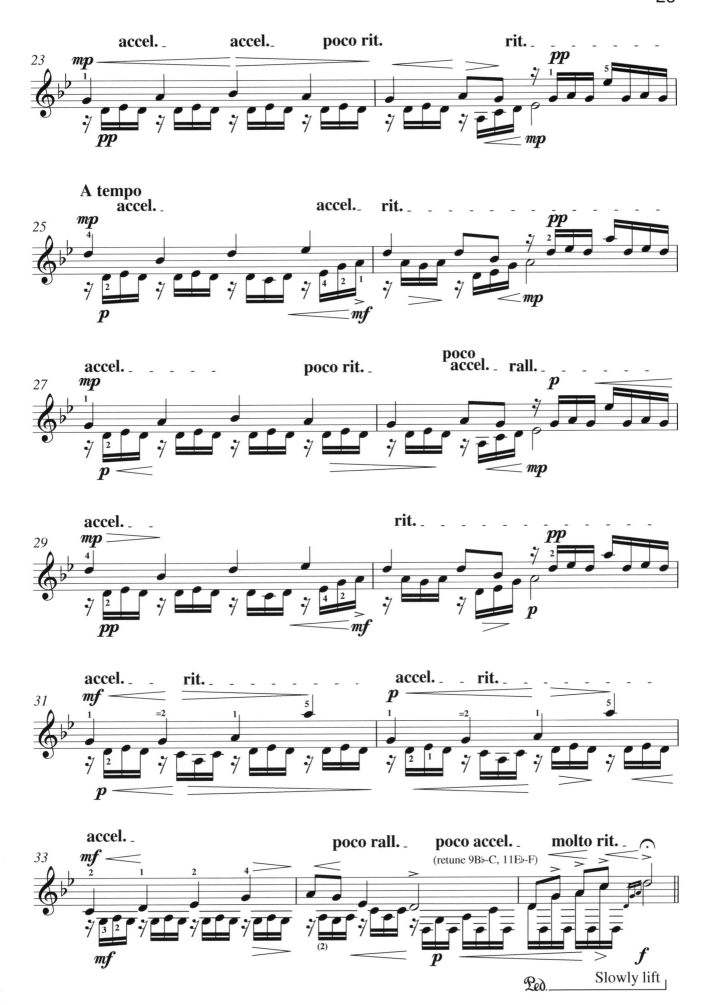

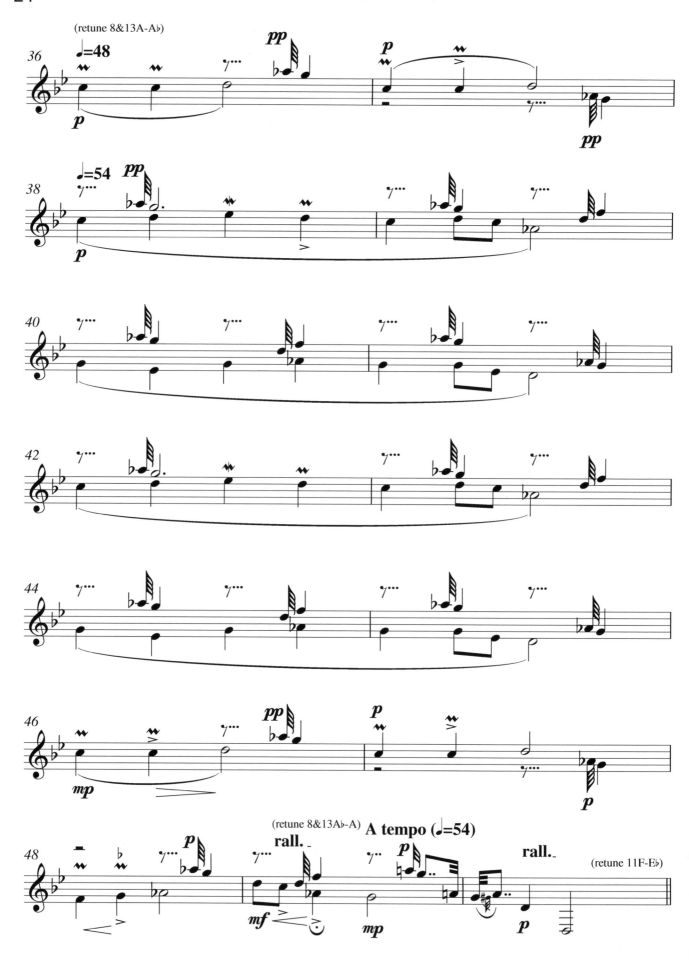

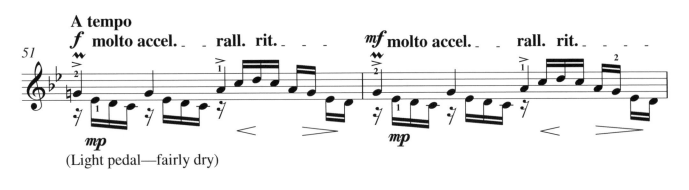

(Light pedal—fairly dry)

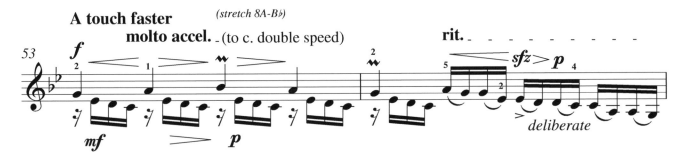

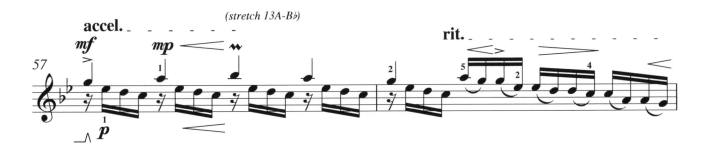

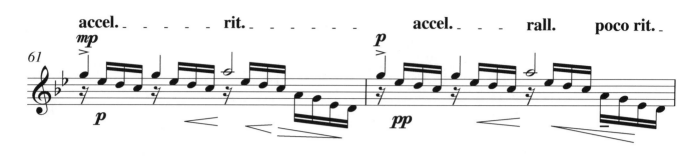

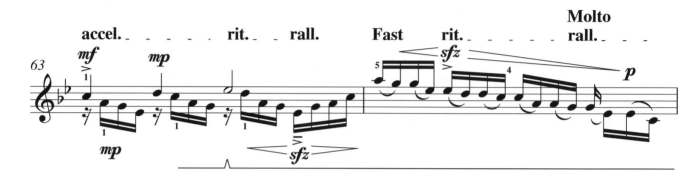

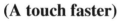

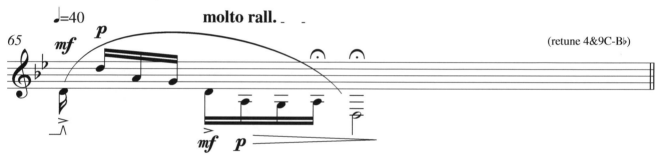

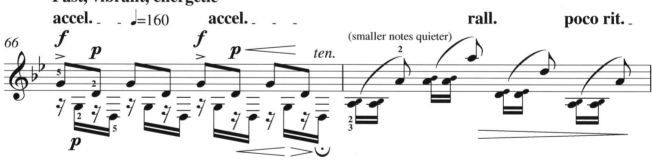

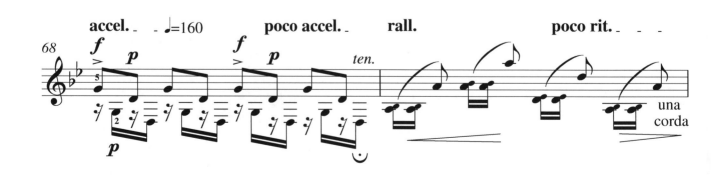

una corda

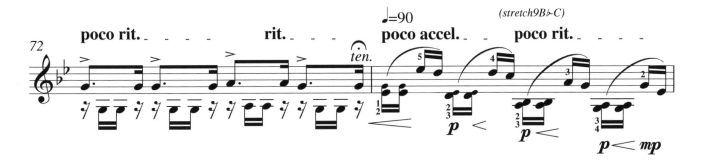

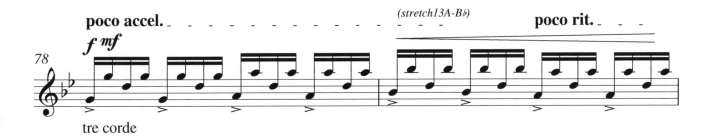

tre corde

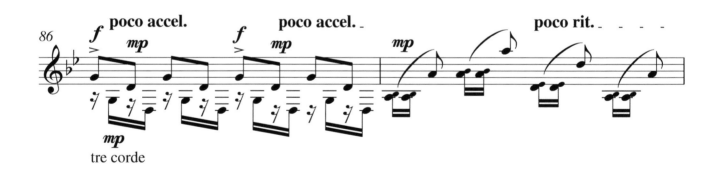

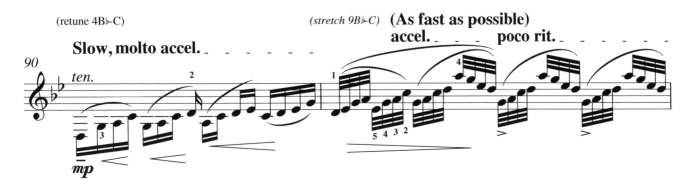

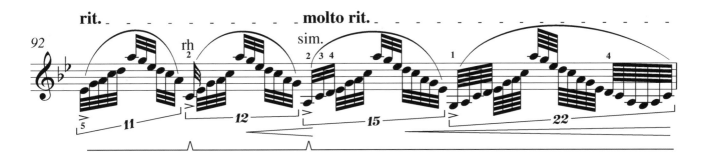

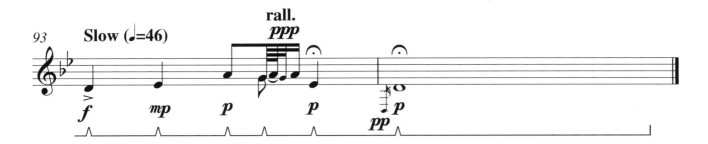

Acknowledgements

My great thanks go to the successors of the three composers Kimio Eto, Tadao Sawai, and Chikushi Katsuko (Hiroyuki Eto, Hikaru Sawai and Kazue Sawai, and the successor of Chikushi Katsuko) for permitting the publication of these arrangements, and to Keisuke Horioka of JASRAC (Japanese Society for the Rights of Authors, Composers and Publishers) and Mitsuki Dazai for facilitating those communications. Also to Hikaru Sawai and Mitsuki Dazai for their very helpful corrections/suggestions for my adaptation of Tadao Sawai's piece *Sakura Sakura.* Also to Masayo Ishigure and Shirley Kazuyo Muramoto for their help in my search for information.

Biographical information on the composers and performers can be found on various websites, including:

- Chikushi Katsuko chikushikai-koto.jp
- Keko Kanagawa kouzan.net
- Kimio Eto nextgenjca.com/kimio-eto
- Shirley Kazuyo Muramoto skmkoto.com
- Tadao Sawai sawaisoukyokuin.com sawai-tadao.jp

The recording of Tadao Sawai's *Sakura Sakura* can be found on track 2 of the CD 箏 名曲選 ~ *Koto Meikyoku Sen (The Best Selections of Koto Music)* which is available to purchase (at time of publication) from hj-how.com/SHOP/1590.html. This is the version I transcribed and adapted for this book. Further track information can be found at komuso.com/albums/albums.pl?album=348. Other performances can be found online, and the version that I initially transcribed was a performance by Tomoko Kawahara—available at youtu.be/UfrBzWMHJJU—and biographical information about her can be found at friendsofkoto.wordpress.com/about.

A list of all these website links can be found at pianoraga.com and there is a playlist of youtube videos of available source materials and performances of the piano transcriptions on my channel youtube.com/intenselypleasant.

APPENDIX A: *Saita-Sakurai* from Francis Taylor Piggott's book *The Music and the Musical Instruments of Japan* B.T. Batsford, London (1893). These pianistic harmonies—his own addition—he felt were implied by the tune.

SAITA-SAKURAI.

4

SAKURA.

Sakura! Sakura!
Yayoi* no sora wa
Mi-watasu kagiri
Kasumi ka kumo ka,
Nioi zo izuru.
Izaya! Izaya!
Mi ni yukan!

KIRSCHBLÜTHE.
Lied mit Koto-Begleitung.
Dies ist das zweite Stück im Lehrplane des jungen Koto-Spielers.
Kirschblüthe! Kirschblüthe!
In dem Lenzeshimmel,
So weit man ihn überblicken kann,
Sind es Nebel oder Wolken?
O nein! denn Blüthenduft verbreitet sich.
Wohlan denn, wohlan denn!
Lasst uns schauen gehen!

* Yayoi = poetischer Ausdruck für den dritten Monat altjapanischer Jahreseintheilung.

CHERRY-BLOSSOMS.
Song with Koto accompaniment.
This is the second tune in the programme of the young Koto-player.
Cherry-blossoms! Cherry-blossoms!
As far as one can see
In the spring heavens,
Is that mist or cloud?
No! for the fragrance of the blossoms diffuses itself.
Come then, come then!
Let us go and see them!

* Yayoi = a poetical expression for the third month of the ancient Japanese calendar.

20313

APPENDIX B: *Sakura* from Rudolph Dittrich's *Nippon Gakufu, Six Japanese Popular Songs collected and arranged for the Pianoforte* Breitkopf and Härtel, Leipzig (1894).

APPENDIX C: *Sakura* from Granville Bantock's *One Hundred Folksongs of All Nations* Oliver Ditson Company, Philadelphia (1911).

Printed in Great Britain
by Amazon